To Ellie and Lenni—
I didn't give you the gift of life, but life gave me
the gift of you. I'm so proud to be your stepmama.

To Jeff—
Thank you for always supporting my dreams.
Thank you for choosing to love. You are
my forever.

2021 Colorado

ISBN Numbers: 978-1-7375249-7-7 hardcover: 978-17375249-8-4

What Makes a Family?

Written by Hannah Bruner   Illustrated by Sandie Sonke

Each family is different. Each family's unique.
So go ahead and turn the page. Come on, let's
take a peek!

When you think of the word "family", you might think of your mom and your dad.

You grew inside mom's tummy

and love baseball just like dad!

Or maybe you think of your foster parents who take good care of you.

They keep you safe and feed you too

and hug you when you're blue.

Perhaps you think of your adoption day, when you found your forever home.

Your new parents kiss you and squeeze you and love you. You know now you're never alone.

Maybe you think of your stepmom who stepped up.

She fell in love with your dad and fell in love
with you too. She makes the best lunches and snuggles you
tight. She shows you you're loved all day and all night!

It could be you think of your stepdad. He's great!

He helps with your homework and makes sure you're never late.

He holds you when you're feeling sad. You call him your "Bonus Dad".

Perhaps you think of your grandparents who raise you. They show you right from wrong and they care through and through!

You might think of
your brother,

your uncle,

your cousin.

Maybe it's your aunt

or your pet bee
named Buzzin.

It could be you think of your sister or godparent.

Maybe it's your friend or your twin or your parrot.

Perhaps you think of your two moms

or two dads.

Or maybe your step-siblings who make you feel glad.

Families become families in all sorts of ways!

Family isn't just sharing DNA or last names. It's not made from getting married or signing a page.
Nope. Not at all.

So then what makes a family? What's one made of?

What makes a family is choosing to

Love

About the Author

Hannah Bruner dreams of a world where all families and familial roles are celebrated. As a seasoned elementary school teacher and stepmama of two wonderful little girls, Hannah knows that families become families in all sorts of ways. Her debut book, What Makes a Family?, endeavors to help readers see mirrors of their own families and discover windows into the families of others.

When Hannah is not teaching, you can find her making memories with her family, strolling the aisles at Target, or eating queso on the patio. Hannah lives in Colorado with her handsome best friend, Jeff, and her two stepdaughters.

Learn more about Hannah here:

www.hannahbruner.com

Follow her on Instagram:

@hannahbrunerbooks

Printed in the USA
CPSIA information can be obtained
at www.ICGtesting.com
LVHW072342261023
762232LV00016B/196